THE HAUNTED
DOT-TO-DOT
HOTEL

Also available by Scoular Anderson,
and published by Young Corgi Books:

THE SPOOKY DOT-TO-DOT
SPACESHIP
MY FIRST JOKE BOOK
THE SPIDER AND CHIPS
JOKE BOOK
SCHOOL JOKES FOR ALIENS

SCOULAR ANDERSON
THE HAUNTED DOT-TO-DOT HOTEL

YOUNG CORGI BOOKS

THE HAUNTED DOT-TO-DOT HOTEL

A YOUNG CORGI BOOK 0 552 527335

First publication in Great Britain

PRINTING HISTORY
Young Corgi edition published 1993

Set in 14/16pt Monotype Baskerville by
Kestrel Data, Exeter

Young Corgi Books are published by Transworld Publishers Ltd, 61-63 Uxbridge Road, Ealing, London W5 5SA, in Australia by Transworld Publishers (Australia) Pty. Ltd, 15-23 Helles Avenue, Moorebank, NSW 2170, and in New Zealand by Transworld Publishers (N.Z.) Ltd, 3 William Pickering Drive, Albany, Auckland.

Made and printed in Great Britain by
Cox & Wyman Ltd, Reading, Berks.

THE HAUNTED
DOT-TO-DOT
HOTEL

A word before you start . . .

Milton was getting ready for a holiday with his dog Hannibal.

Join the dots •1 to •73

Use a curved line where you see this •⌣

Use a jaggy line ⋀⋀ where you see this •⋀

He was looking forward to being in the open air.

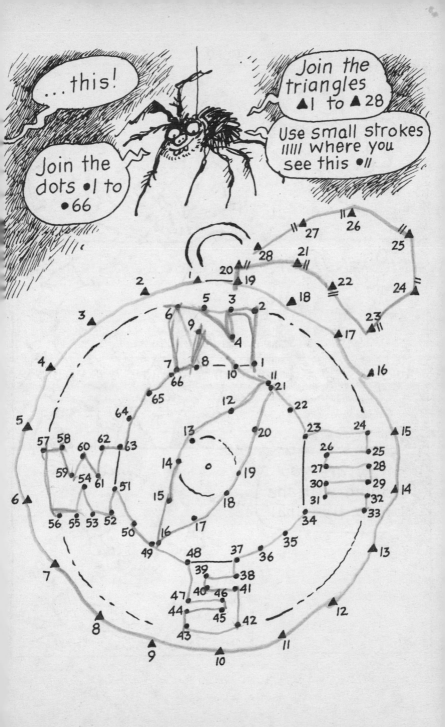

Milton was almost ready to go.

He decided Hannibal needed some
energy.

They set out at last.

They walked for an hour and a half.

Until . . .

The names have worn off the signpost
Join the dots •1 to •51
Use a curved line where you see this
Use small strokes where you see this

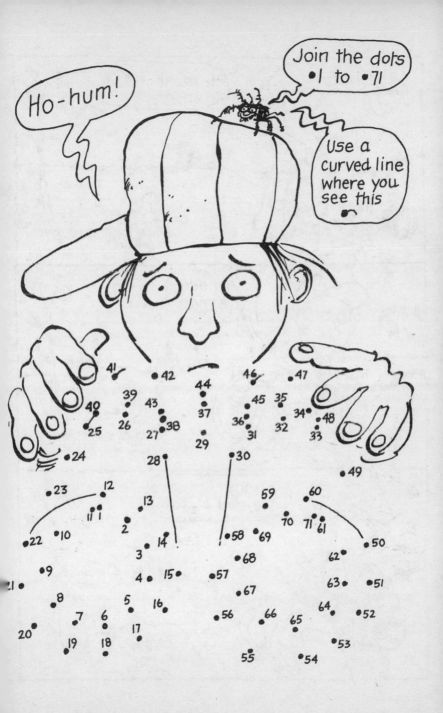

Milton tried to find his way without the map.

But . . .

He was getting confused.

But the road grew narrower and narrower.

At last they came to a clearing in the
woods.

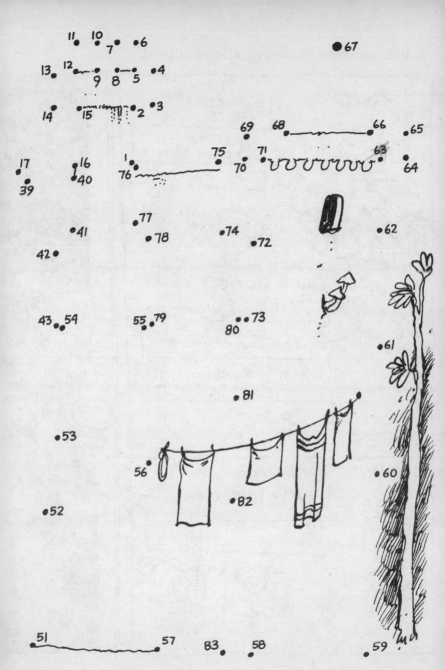

It was just what the weary Milton wanted.

Join the dots •1 to •49

Hello?

DING! DING!

RECEPTION

The manager appeared.

Elvis led the way upstairs. Hannibal was
sure he felt something move.

Nothing in this hotel was quite as it seemed.

Elvis showed Milton his room.

But Milton was feeling tired.

After a while, Milton came downstairs to eat.

But supper seemed a bit restless.

There was still more to come . . .

. . . and it was so good Milton had three helpings.

The hotel staff were terribly pleased.

Milton was certainly dreaming . . .

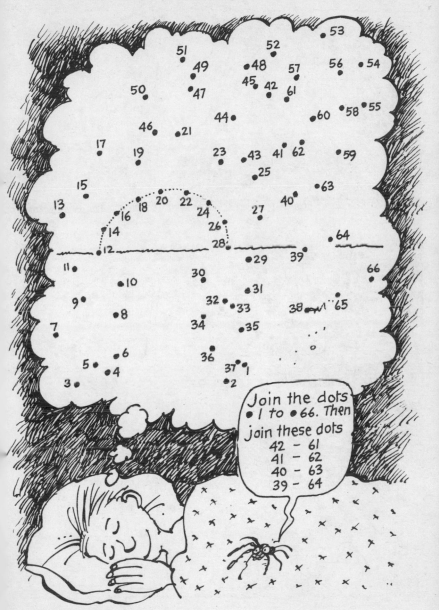

. . . and so was Hannibal.

Next morning . . .

They went downstairs . . .

. . . and into the dining room.

Mr Drizzle didn't like what he heard.

Nasturtium and Elvis swung into action.

Breakfast turned out to be even more
lively than supper.

Suddenly . . .

Join the
dots
•1 to •82

Milton still didn't seem worried.

Mr Drizzle, Nasturtium and Elvis were
not amused.

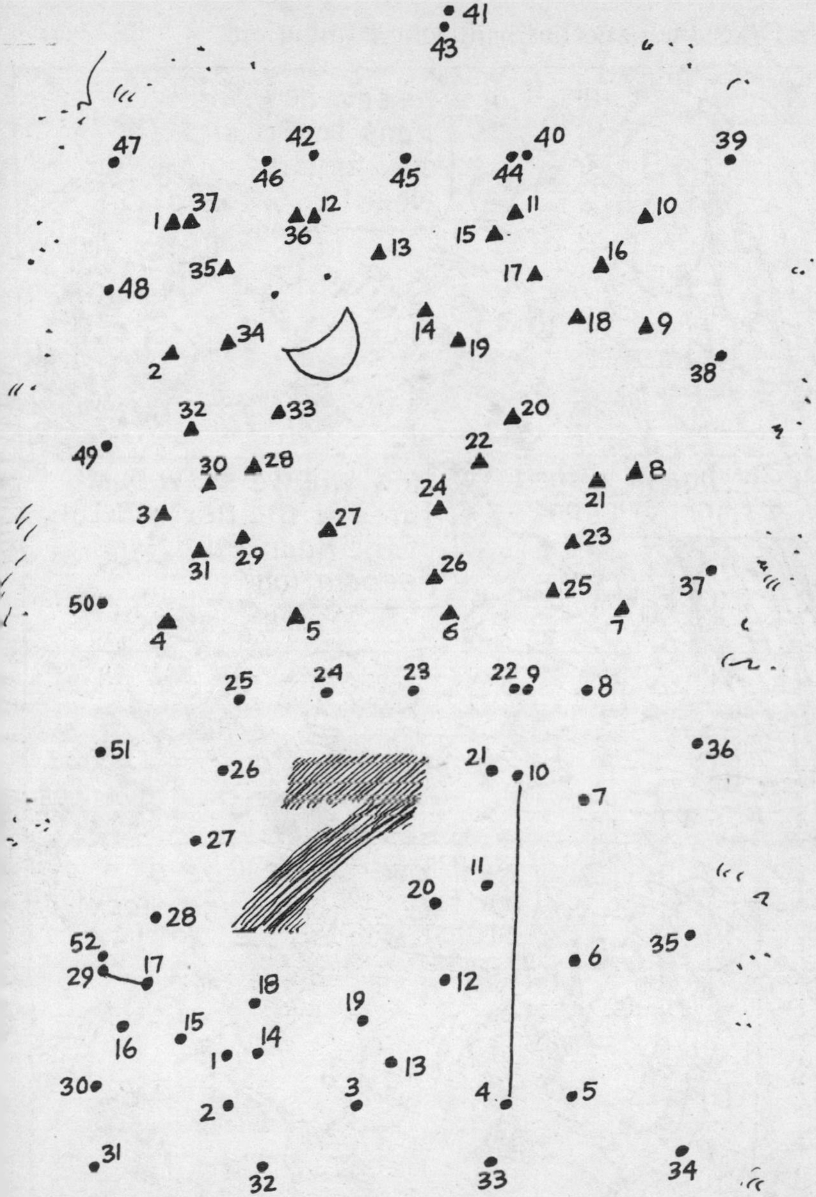

Mr Drizzle felt another headache coming on.

So Mr Drizzle made a decision.

Nasturtium had some doubts.

They arrived at the werewolf's den.

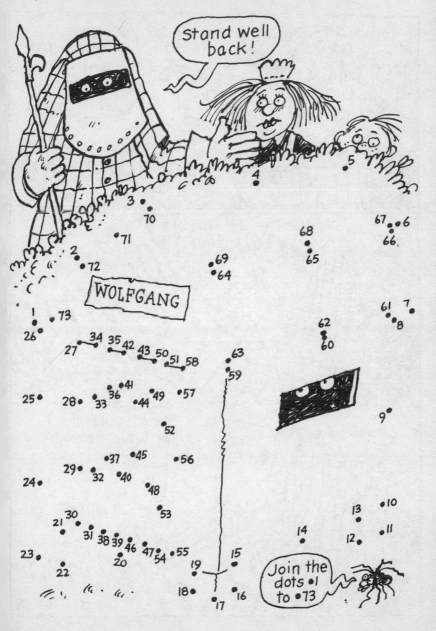

Mr Drizzle called to the werewolf.

With another spine-chilling howl, the werewolf appeared.

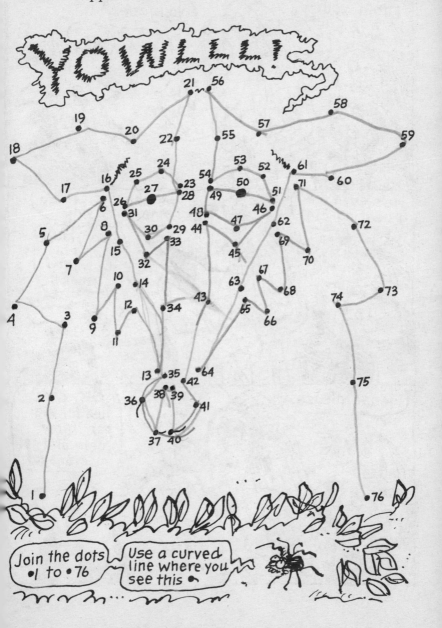

They were rather disappointed.

But just as they reached the hotel . . .

. . . something unfortunate happened.

The vet arrived in next to no time.

Mr Scrimbag the vet examined Wolfgang.

Mr Scrimbag gave Mr Drizzle,
Nasturtium and Elvis something to help
them relax.

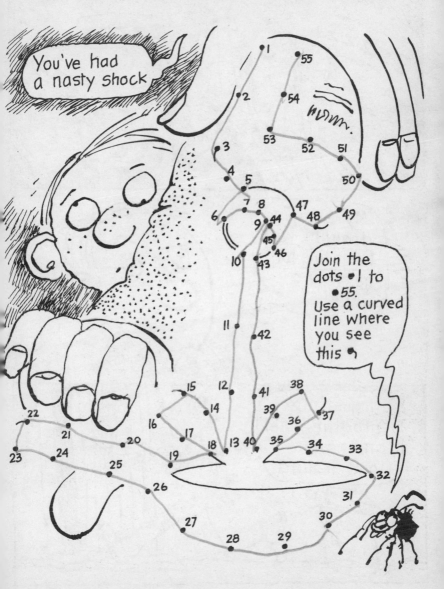

The staff of Slimecrag were certainly relaxed.

He saw something that took his fancy.

But something horrible jumped out of the
barrel towards Mr Scrimbag.

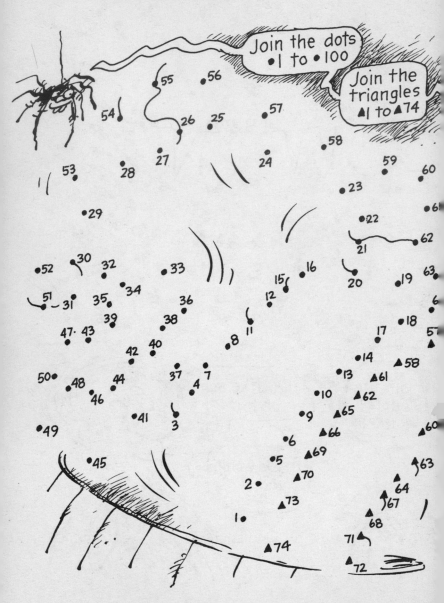

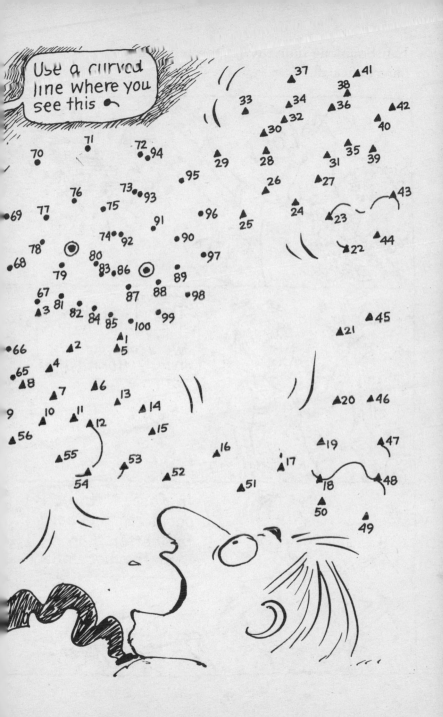

Mr Scrimbag didn't want to stay in the hotel after all.

Milton took something to revive the drowsy staff with.

Milton had already made some plans . . .

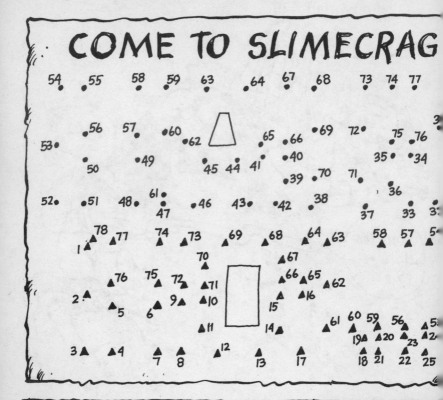

. . . and some posters.

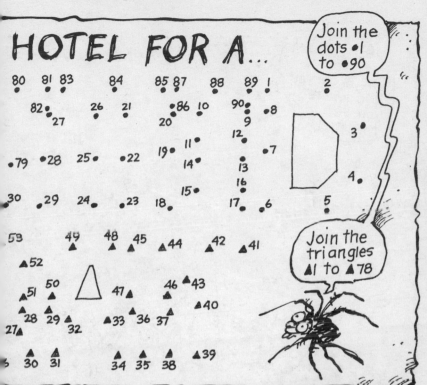

Milton's plan was put into action.

In a few months, people were arriving by the bus-load for scary weekends.

So if you ever stop off at the Slimecrag
Hotel . . .

. . . you have been warned!